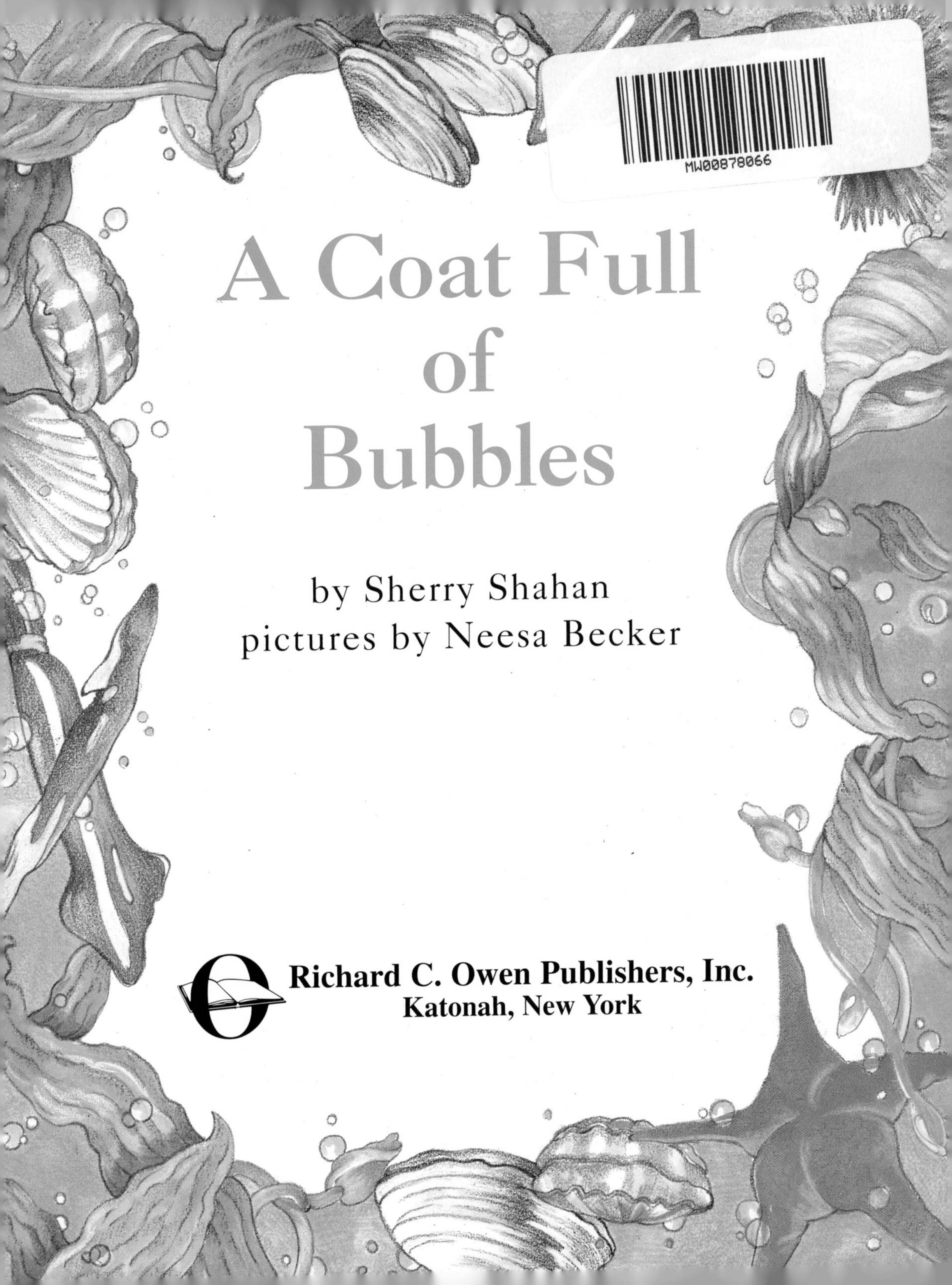

A Coat Full of Bubbles

by Sherry Shahan
pictures by Neesa Becker

Richard C. Owen Publishers, Inc.
Katonah, New York

The sea otter loves
to play in the sea.

She floats.

She dives.

She hides in the seaweed.

The sea otter has
a thick coat of fur.

She rolls.

She scratches.
She fluffs up her fur.

Soon her fur coat is
full of bubbles–

hundreds and hundreds of tiny air bubbles.

A coat full of bubbles keeps
the sea otter warm and snug,
so she can play all day in the sea.